JAM JAM JAM

with
PAUL KOSSOFF

Professional Guitar Workshops

Exclusive Distributors:
Music Sales Limited
8/9 Frith Street
London W1V 5TZ England

Music Sales Pty Limited
120 Rothschild Avenue
Rosebery, NSW 2018
Australia

Order No AM959838 Jam with Paul Kossoff ISBN 0-7119-7799-2
This book © Copyright 2000 by Wise Publications

www.musicsales.com

Cover Design by Kim Waller
Music engraved by Cambridge Notation

Printed in the United Kingdom by
Caligraving Limited, Thetford, Norfolk.

Your Guarantee of Quality

As publishers we strive to produce every book to the highest commercial standards. The music has been
freshly engraved and the book has been carefully designed to minimise awkward page turns and to make
playing from it a real pleasure. Particular care has been given to specifying acid-free, neutral-sized paper
made from pulps which have not been elemental chlorine bleached. This pulp is from farmed sustainable
forests and was produced with special regard for the environment.
Throughout, the printing and binding have been planned to ensure a sturdy, attractive publication which
should give years of enjoyment. If your copy fails to meet our high standards, please inform us and we will
gladly replace it.

Music Sales' complete catalogue describes thousands of titles and is available in full colour sections by
subject, direct from Music Sales Limited. Please state your areas of interest and send a cheque/postal
order for £1.50 for postage to: Music Sales Limited, Newmarket Road, Bury St Edmunds, Suffolk IP33 3YD.

Wise Publications
London/New York/Sydney/Paris/Copenhagen/Madrid/Tokyo

CONTENTS

Introduction   4

Performance notes   5

Tablature explanation   7

All right now   8

The hunter   16

Mister big   27

Wishing well   33

Fire and water   40

My brother jake   46

The stealer   52

I'm a mover   58

ON THE CD

The CD is split into two sections; section 1 (tracks 1-8) is the backing tracks minus lead guitar & vocals, while section 2 (tracks 9-16) is the backing tracks with all guitar parts added, so in addition to the written tab you can hear the rhythm, fills and solos as they should be played!

Music arranged and produced by Stuart Bull and Steve Finch.
Recorded at the TOTAL ACCURACY SOUNDHOUSE, Romford, England.

Richard Barrett: guitar.
Mick Ash: bass.
Alison Pearse: keyboards.
Steve Finch: Drums/percussion.

Music transcribed by Richard Barrett

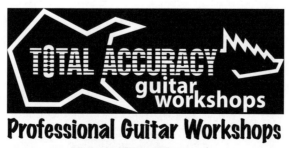

Professional Guitar Workshops

Visit the Total Accuracy
Audio Visual Experience at
http://www.totalaccuracy.co.uk

Introduction

THE TOTAL ACCURACY 'JAM WITH...' series is a powerful learning tool that will help you extend your stockpile of licks and fills and develop your improvisational skills. The combination of musical notation and guitar tablature in the book, together with backing tracks on the CD, gives you the opportunity to learn each track note for note and then jam with a professional session band. The track listing reflects some of Free's most popular recordings, providing something for guitarists to have fun with and improvise with, as well as something to aspire to.

The first eight tracks on the CD are full length backing tracks recorded minus lead guitar. The remaining tracks feature the backing tracks with the lead guitar parts added. Although many of you will have all the original tracks in your own collections, we have provided them in the package for your reference. The 'JAM WITH...' series allows you to accurately recreate the original, or to use the transcriptions in this book in conjunction with the backing tracks as a basis for your own improvisation. For your benefit we have put definite endings on the backing tracks, rather than fading them out as is the case on some of the original recordings. The accompanying transcriptions correspond to our versions. Remember, experimenting with your own ideas is equally important for developing your own style; most important of all, however, is that you enjoy JAM with FREE and HAVE FUN!

Formed in 1968, the four members of Free all came from similar musical backgrounds. Paul Kossoff and Simon Kirke were playing semi-professionally with a blues band named Black Cat Bone, Andy Fraser was with John Mayall's Bluesbreakers and Paul Rodgers led a blues outfit called Brown Sugar. They were all based in the London area and were, to varying degrees, starting to tire of the blues boom which had been sweeping Britain.

When Kossoff and Kirke decided to form their own band they were impressed by the vocal style of Paul Rodgers and a jam session at a Brown Sugar gig secured his place as vocalist. In the meantime, a mutual friend had told Andy Fraser about a great young guitarist he knew, from a band who were looking for a bass player . . .

The first time all four members played together was in a pub called The Nag's Head in Battersea. Apparently, they wrote four songs that very night! Later, Fraser would comment; "the excitement created between us lasted quite a long while for me". During the early days, Free were taken under the wing of blues afficionado Alexis Korner, who suggested the name, spread the word and included the young band on many of his club dates.

This exposure led to a contract with Island Records and the release of their debut album, Tons Of Sobs. This was followed by Free, then the classic Fire And Water. The follow up, Highway, was disappointing in terms of sales and pressure began to build for another hit single. This eventually led to a parting of the ways and subsequent spin-offs like 'Kossoff, Kirke, Tetsu and Rabbit'. None of the members of Free experienced the same success apart as they had together, so they reformed and recorded a fifth album, Free At Last. The subsequent tour did not run smoothly, due to tensions between the band members (Kossoff was frequently too ill to perform, the legacy of his worsening drug habit). The band held together long enough to record a final album, Heartbreaker, though Kossoff was not on all of the tracks, due to persistent health problems and he was eventually replaced on tour by Wendell Richardson, from the band Osibisa.

When the band split this time, it was for good. Paul Rodgers and Simon Kirke went on to great success with Bad Company, Andy Fraser joined up with top session guitarist Chris Spedding, to form Sharks and Paul Kossoff put together his own band, Back Street Crawler. In March 1976, he was flying from Los Angeles to New York when he died of a heart attack. The recordings he left behind are still a source of inspiration to millions of guitarists.

Performance Notes

All Right Now

The band's biggest hit, this track was apparently written in some haste, to make up the running time of the Fire And Water album! The verses feature Paul's doubled rhythm guitars with only the drums for accompaniment, with the bass kicking in for the choruses and solo. There are various stories in circulation about what guitar was used to get this classic sound, but it seems likely that it was a Gibson Les Paul with the bridge pickup selected, through Marshall amps and cabs. The most important aspect when attempting to recreate this tone is not to use too much distortion, or low end.

The Hunter

Paul Kossoff's amazing vibrato technique is well in evidence during the opening seconds of this track, playing a melodic pattern based around the A blues scale; (A, C, D, E♭, E, G). The verse sections feature some economic staccato chord stabs, occasionally varying the rhythm slightly to avoid being too repetitive. The solo section begins with a developing repeated figure, building in intensity - even adding a second lead guitar in the final section, which is included on the backing track. The track closes in a similar fashion to the intro, with the main theme being repeated. To get his chunky overdriven tone, Paul used a Gibson Les Paul through Marshall amps.

Mister Big

A track of epic proportions, built around a funky bass and guitar riff. LIke several other tracks, Kossoff has overdubbed more than one guitar part, which is reflected on the backing track, leaving you free to play all the main parts, including the marathon solo! Here, open and high fretted strings are mixed in the latter half, giving a jangling, yet powerful sound. Like many of the other tracks, there is little doubt that Kossoff is using the classic Les Paul/Marshall set up.

Wishing Well

From the later part of the band's career, this track features aggressive, distorted backing guitars, under the soulful lead playing. Tricks featured here include wide string bends, staccato picking attack and repetitive high register phrasing. Though there are several guitar overdubs on the original, the backing track is arranged so that you get to play all the most important rhythm and lead guitar parts. The solo sections appear to have been played through a Univibe, or a similar effect. The tone is slightly more distorted that the earlier material, though still almost certainly a Les Paul through a Marshall amp.

Fire And Water

Featuring Paul's classic Les Paul tone, this track makes good use of both ringing open and fretted power chords. The overdrive tone is the result of sheer volume, rather than boosting the tone with pedals. The infinitely sustaining notes in the solo reinforce this point further, though these are aided by a wide, distinctive vibrato. It is interesting to note that Kossoff's guitar is rarely heard with any reverb or other effects, appearing on the record just as it came from the amplifier, which was once again probably a Marshall.

My Brother Jake

Heavily featuring piano in the mix, there is a deceptive amount of clever guitar work here from Kossoff, apart from the more readily discernible lead guitar frills. It is rumoured that this track was played on a Fender Stratocaster now owned by Iron Maiden's Dave Murray. In any case, use the neck pickup for all the chord work, with an almost completely clean tone, reverting to a more typical blues crunch on the bridge pickup for the lead guitar parts. This track was probably played using Marshall amps and cabs.

The Stealer

A tightly arranged production, with several guitar overdubs, this track could almost have been played using the neck pickup of a Strat, though the classic Les Paul lead tone finds its way in towards the end! The repetitive nature of the verse rhythm part makes it quite challenging, as the timing and phrasing need to be consistent. This feel is broken away from during the guitar solo and outro, where ringing chords sit over the driving bass and drums. This track was probably played using Kossoff's customary Marshall set up.

I'm A Mover

Built around a crunching, repetitive guitar riff during the verse, the chorus abruptly switches to the neck pickup for some shrill blues soloing alongside Paul Rodgers' vocal. This track is a great showcase for Kossoff's playing, featuring many trademarks like the wide vibrato, repeated bend and pre-bend licks and staccato phrasing. The tone, as on most of these tracks, is pure Les Paul through a Marshall amp. Though the original version features overdubbed lead guitars, the backing track is arranged so that you can play all the main lead and rhythm parts in one performance.

Notation & Tablature Explained

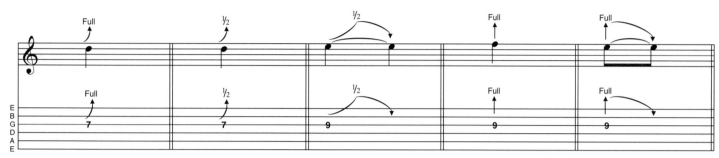

BEND: Strike the note and bend up a whole step (two frets).

BEND: Strike the note and bend up a half step (one fret).

BEND AND RELEASE: Strike the note, bend up a half step, then release the bend.

PRE-BEND: Bend the note up, then strike it.

PRE-BEND AND RELEASE: Bend up, strike the note, then release it.

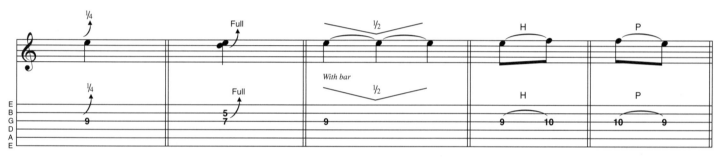

QUARTER-TONE BEND: Bend the note slightly sharp.

UNISON BEND: Strike both notes, then bend the lower note up to the pitch of the higher one.

TREMOLO BAR BENDS: Strike the note, and push the bar down and up by the amounts indicated.

HAMMER-ON: Strike the first note, then sound the second by fretting it without picking.

PULL-OFF: Strike the higher note, then pull the finger off while keeping the lower one fretted.

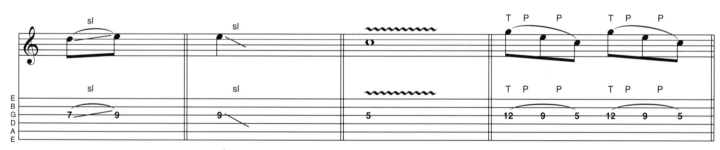

SLIDE: Slide the finger from the first note to the second. Only the first note is struck.

SLIDE: Slide to the fret from a few frets below or above.

VIBRATO: The string is vibrated by rapidly bending and releasing a note with the fretboard hand or tremolo bar.

TAPPING: Hammer on to the note marked with a T using the picking hand, then pull off to the next note, following the hammer-ons or pull-offs in the normal way.

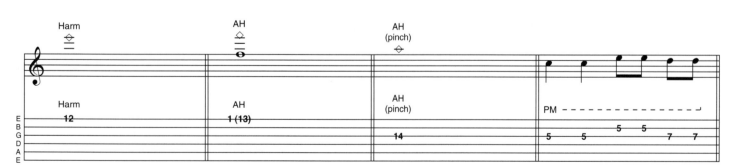

NATURAL HARMONIC: Lightly touch the string directly over the fret shown, then strike the note to create a "chiming" effect.

ARTIFICIAL HARMONIC: Fret the note, then use the picking hand finger to touch the string at the position shown in brackets and pluck with another finger.

ARTIFICIAL HARMONIC: The harmonic is produced by using the edge of the picking hand thumb to "pinch" the string whilst picking firmly with the plectrum.

PALM MUTES: Rest the palm of the picking hand on the strings near the bridge to produce a muted effect. Palm mutes can apply to a single note or a number of notes (shown with a dashed line).

All Right Now

Words & Music by
Paul Rodgers & Andy Fraser

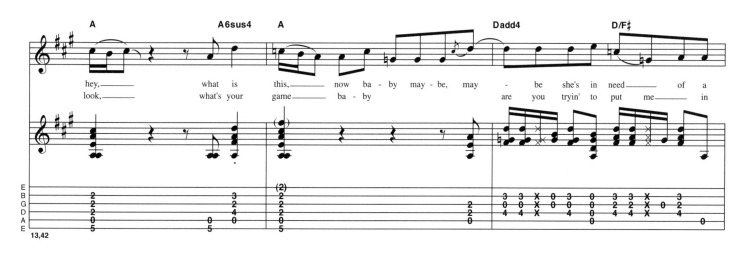

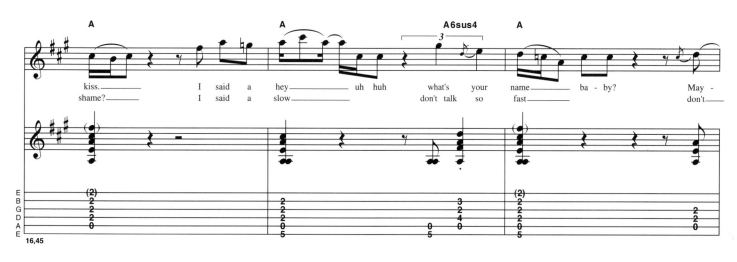

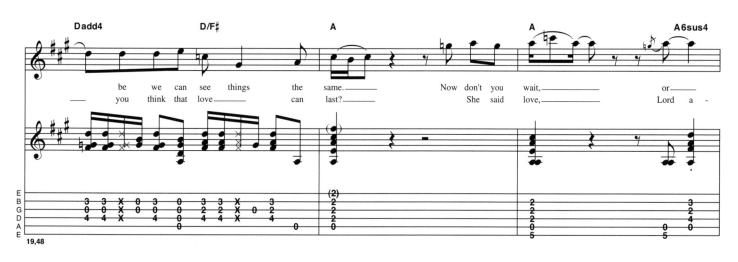

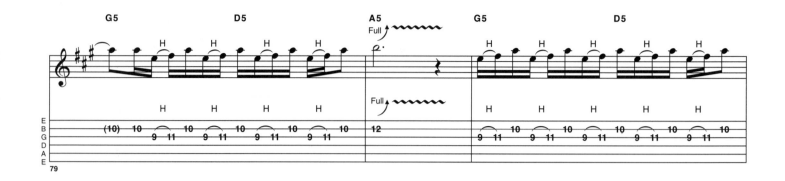

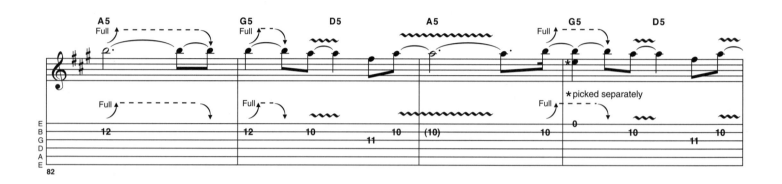

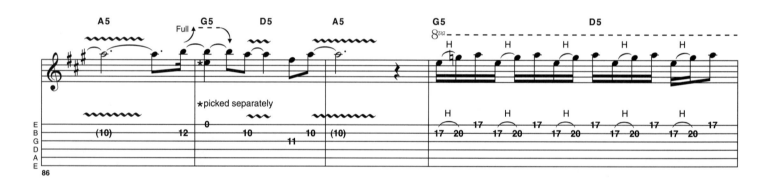

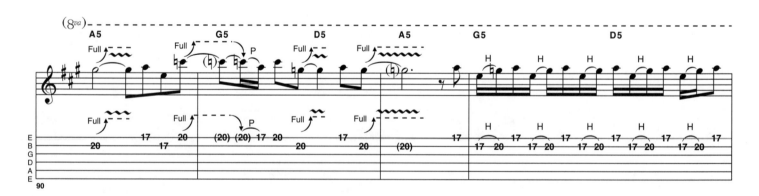

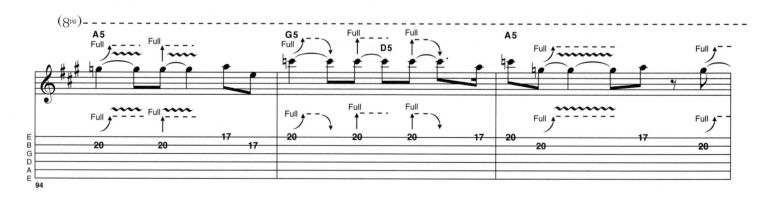

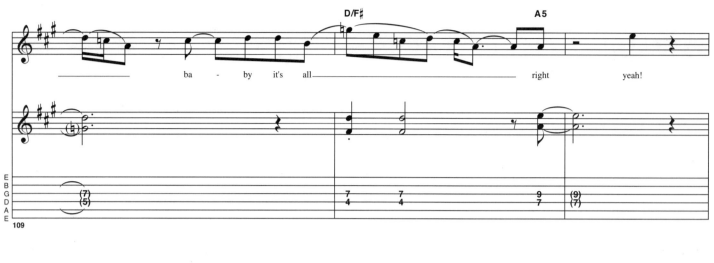

ba - by it's all _____ right   yeah!

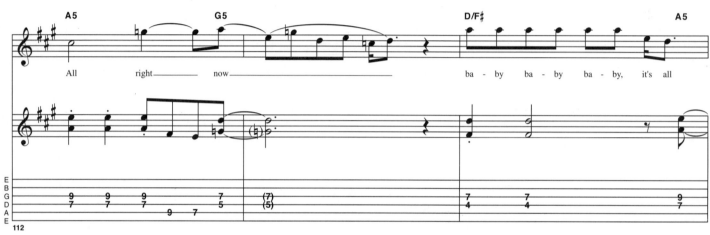

All   right _____ now _____   ba - by ba - by ba - by,   it's all

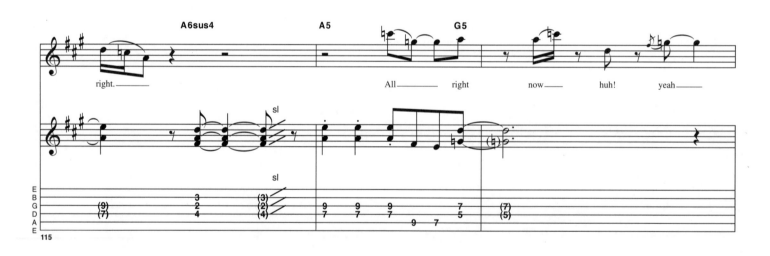

right. _____   All _____ right   now _____ huh!   yeah _____

it's   all   right   it's   all   right   it's   all   right   yeah!   right _____ now _____

The Hunter

Words & Music by
Booker T. Jones, Carl Wells,
Steve Cropper, Donald Dunn & Al Jackson Jr.

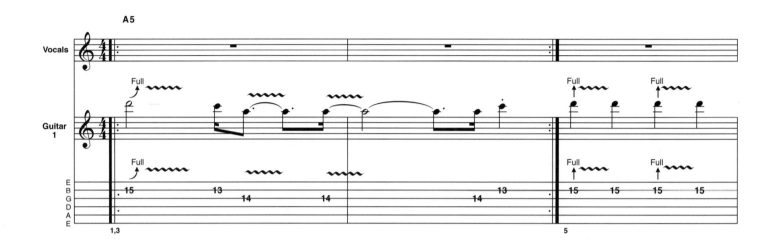

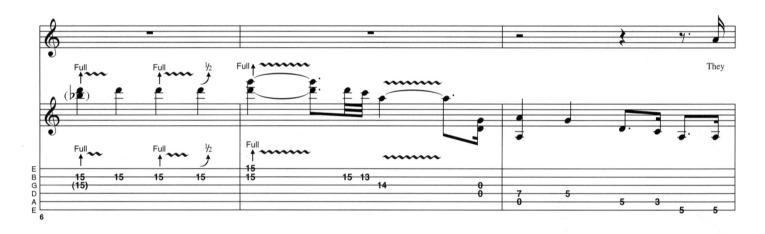

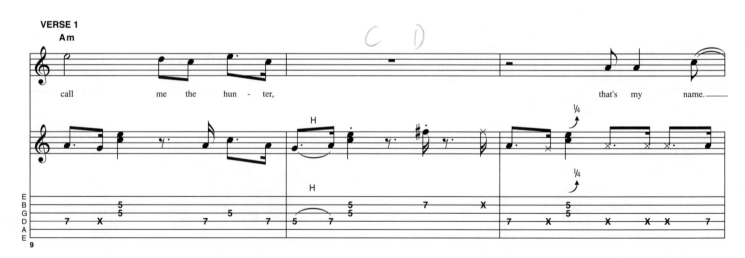

A pret - ty lit - tle wo - man like you

is my on - ly game._____ I bought me a love_____

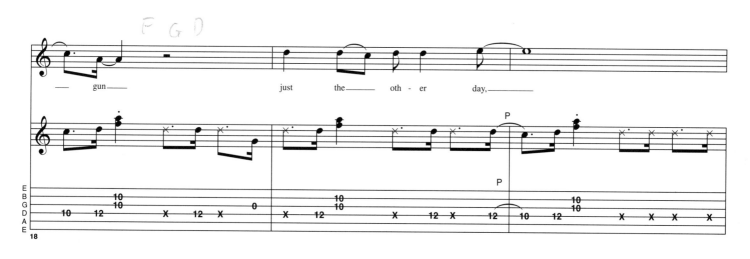

___ gun ___ just the ___ oth - er day, _____

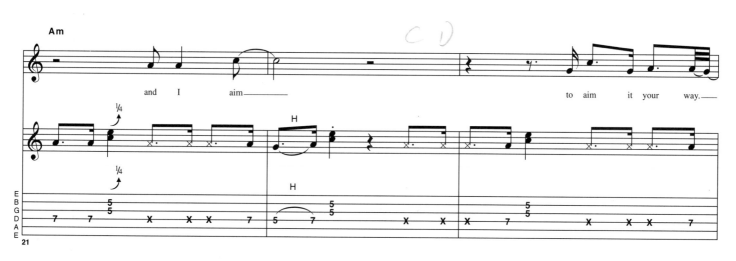

and I aim _____ to aim it your way. _____

CHORUS 2

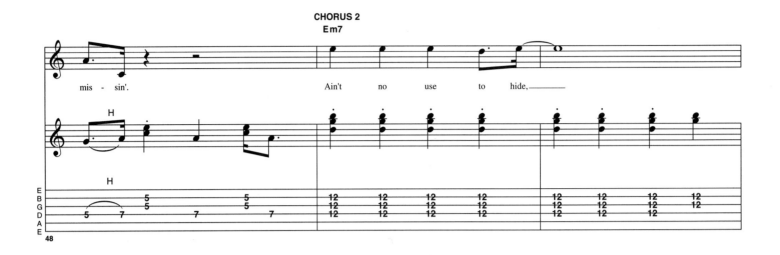

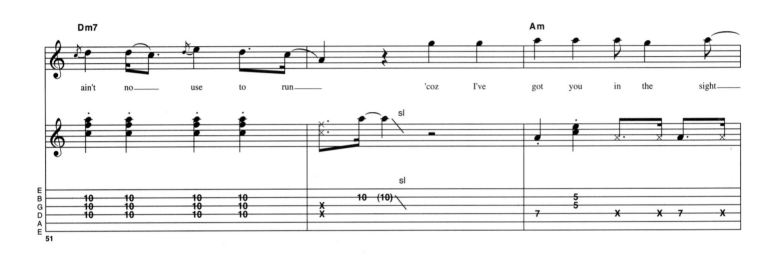

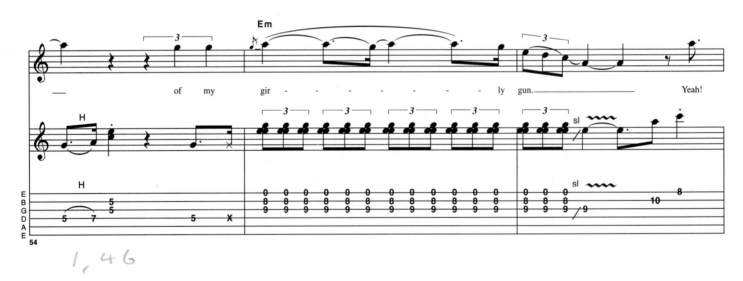

1, 46

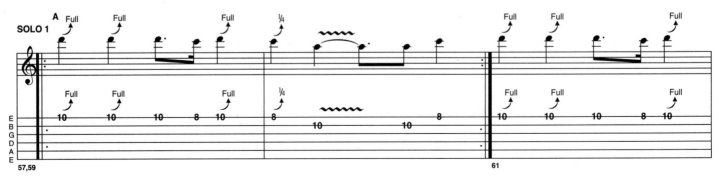

20

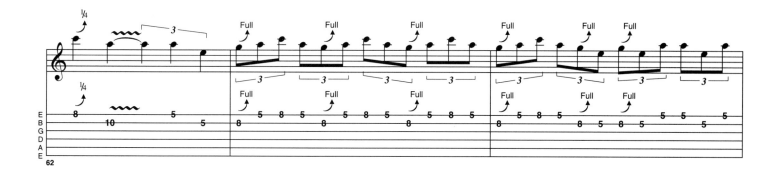

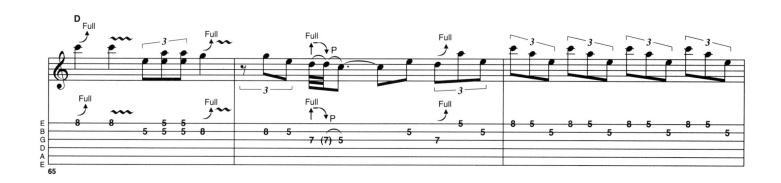

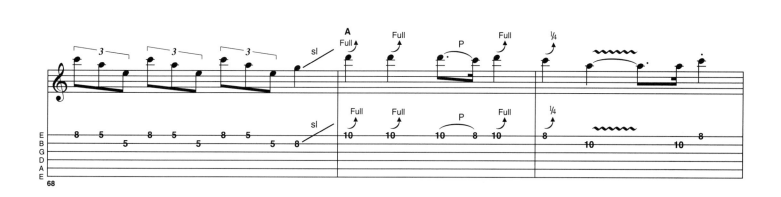

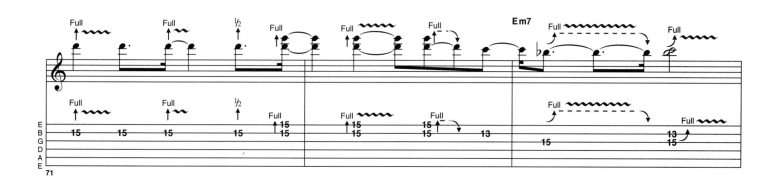

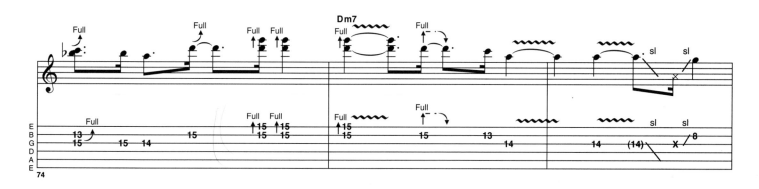

Second part

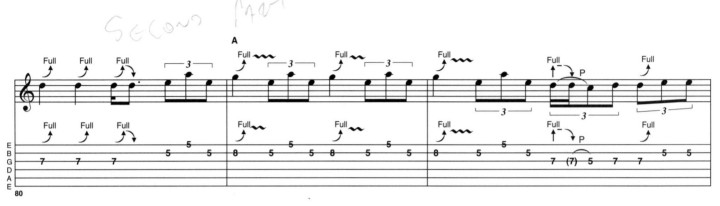

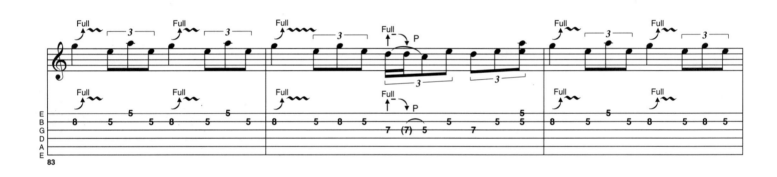

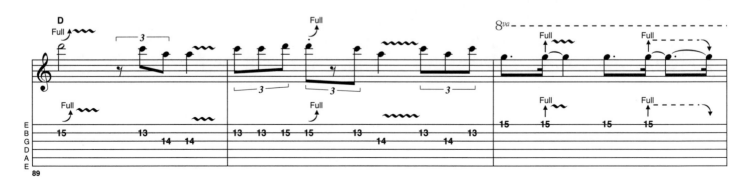

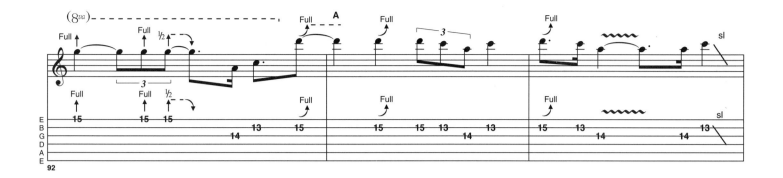

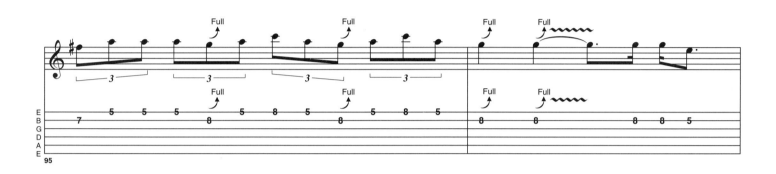

CHORUS 3

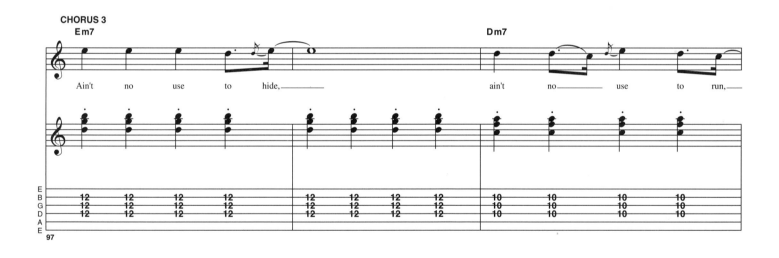

Ain't no use to hide, ain't no use to run,

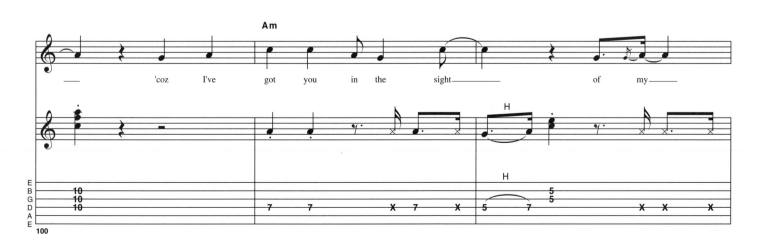

'coz I've got you in the sight of my

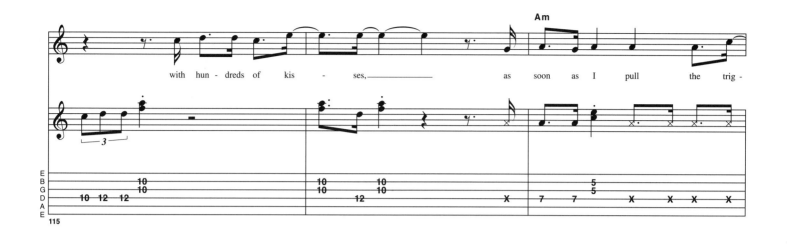

with hun - dreds of kis - ses,＿＿＿＿ as soon as I pull the trig -

＿ ger ba - by there will be＿＿＿ no mis - sin'.

CHORUS 4

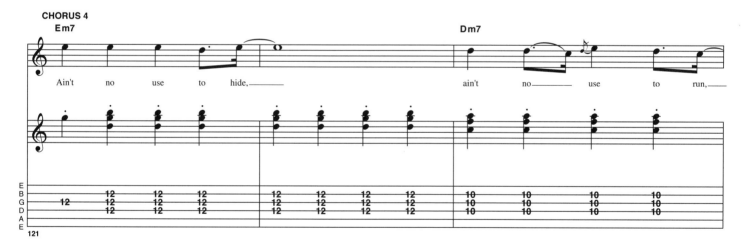

Ain't no use to hide,＿＿＿ ain't no＿＿＿ use to run,＿＿＿

＿＿ 'coz I've got you in the sight＿＿＿ of my

gir - - - - - - ly gun.

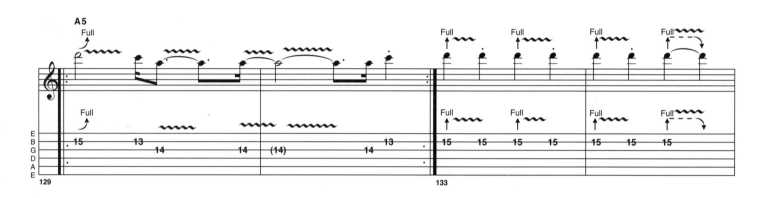

A5

Mister Big

Words & Music by
Paul Rodgers, Andy Fraser,
Simon Kirke & Paul Kossoff

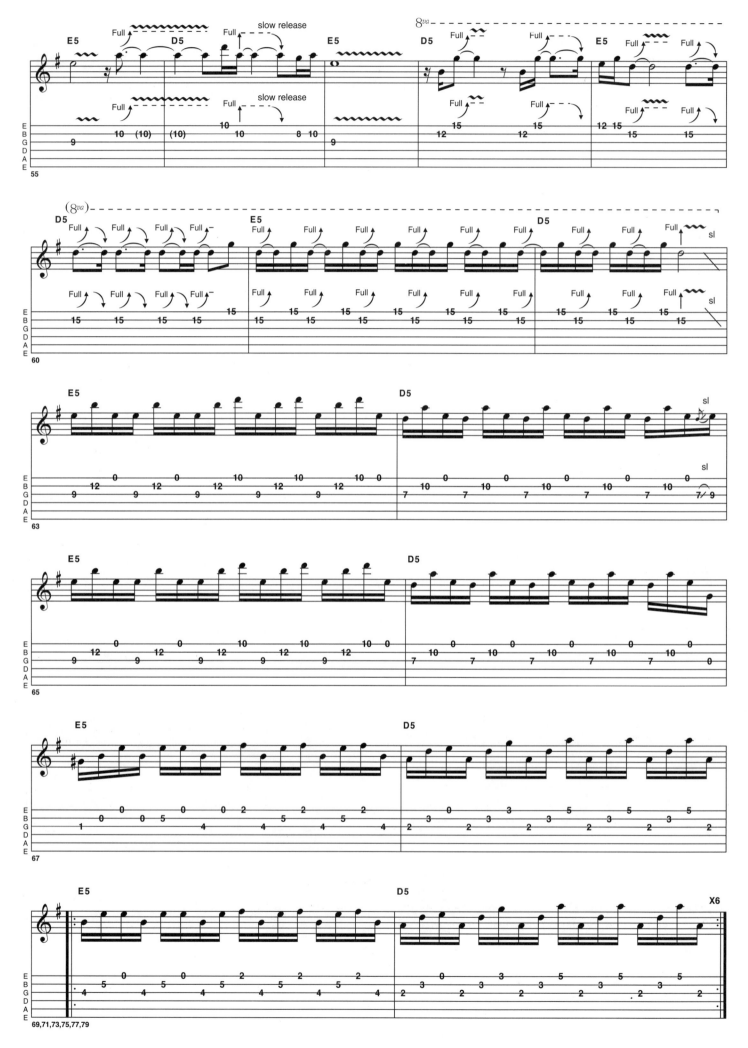

Wishing Well

Words & Music by
Paul Rodgers, Simon Kirke,
Tetsu Yamauchi, John Bundrick & Paul Kossoff

12 G

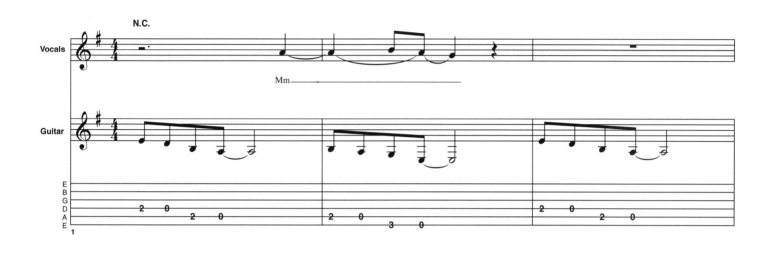

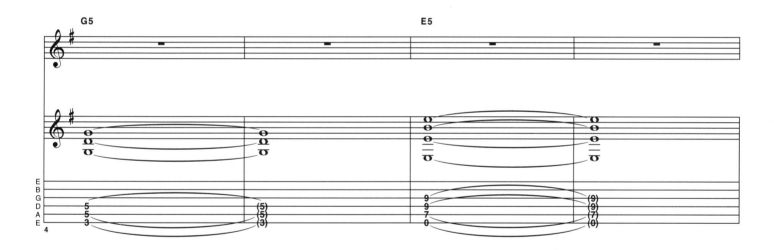

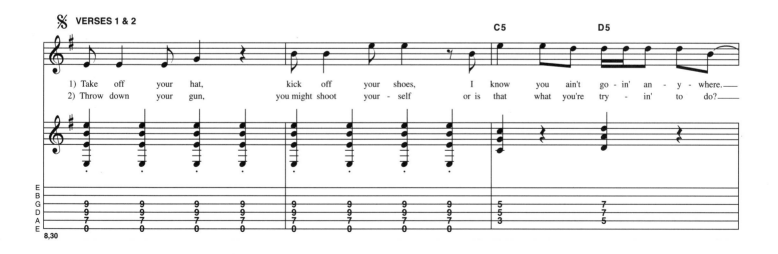

1) Take off your hat, kick off your shoes, I know you ain't go-in' an-y-where.
2) Throw down your gun, you might shoot your-self or is that what you're try-in' to do?

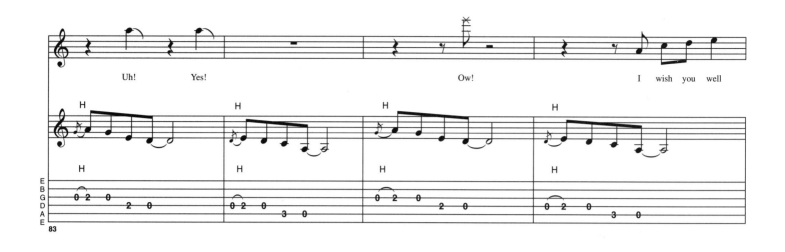

Uh!   Yes!   Ow!   I wish you well

Ooh————— the wish-ing well   ow!   Ev' - ry bo-

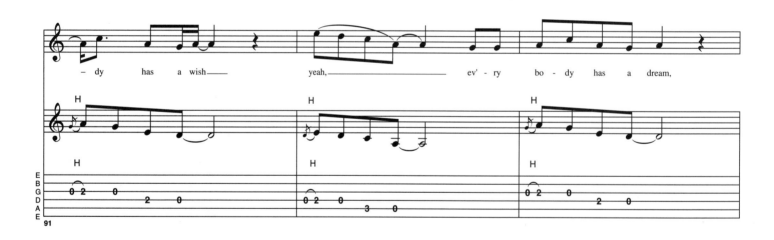

- dy has a wish—— yeah,————— ev' - ry bo - dy has a dream,

yeah———————— yeah—— wish you well   ow!   Let's dream——

OUTRO SOLO

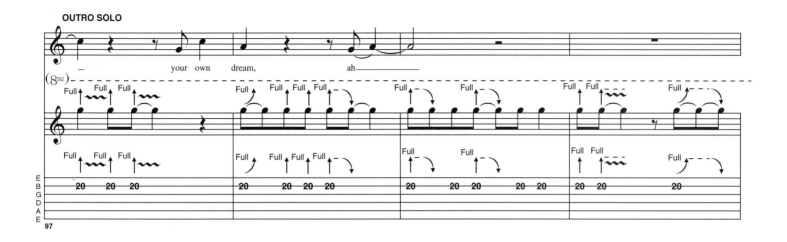

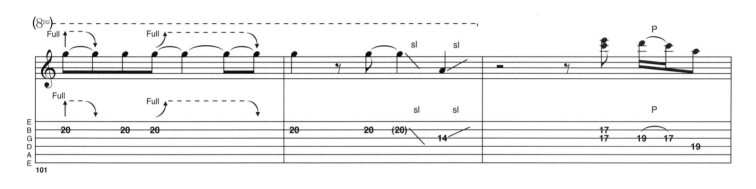

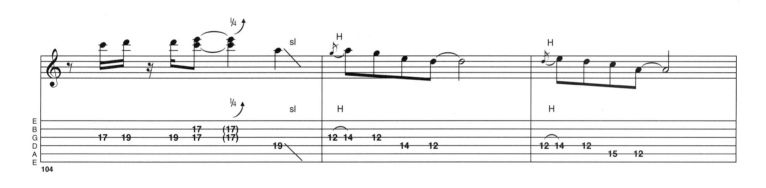

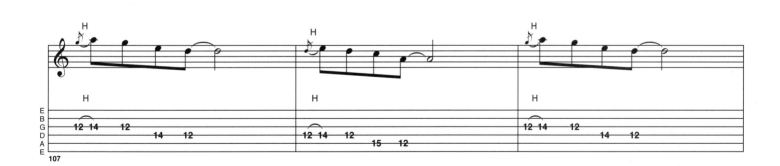

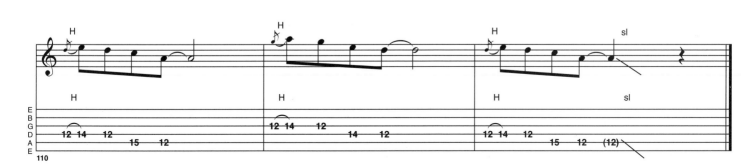

Fire And Water

Words & Music by
Paul Rodgers & Andy Fraser

13G

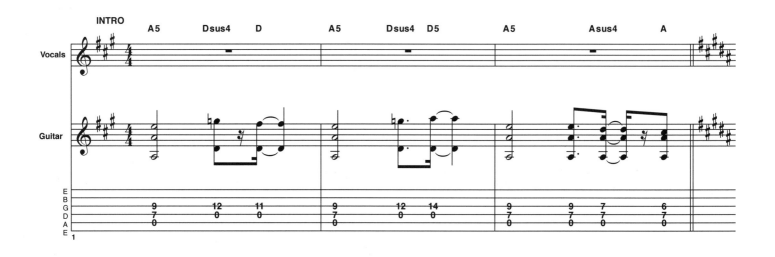

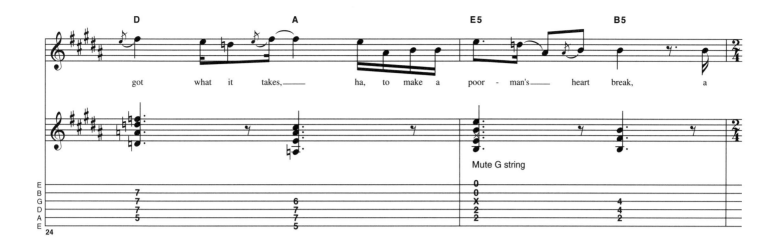

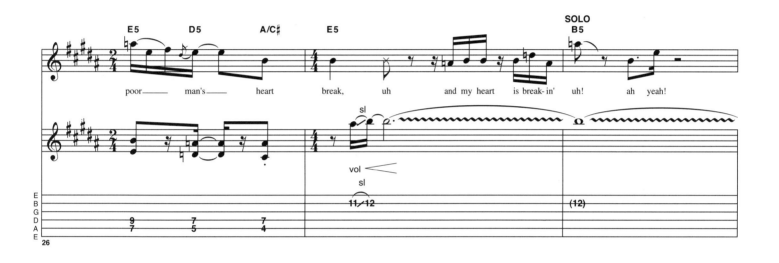

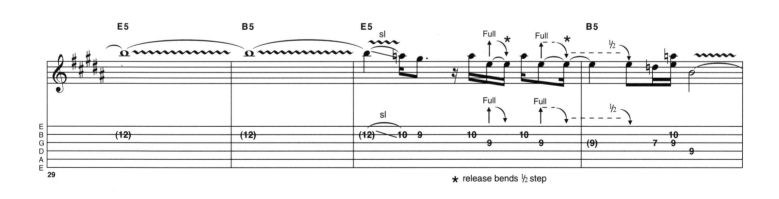

★ release bends ½ step

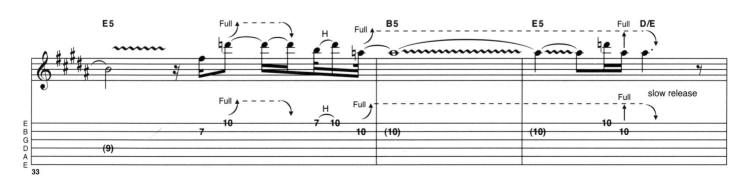

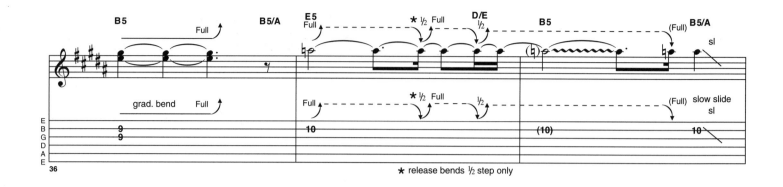

★ release bends ½ step only

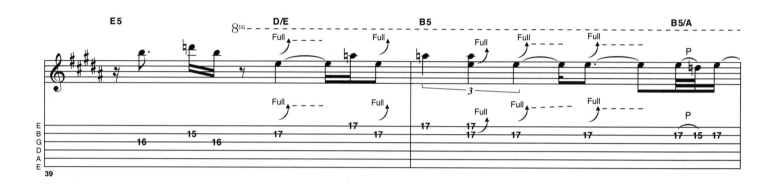

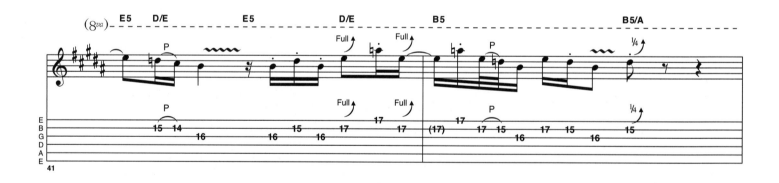

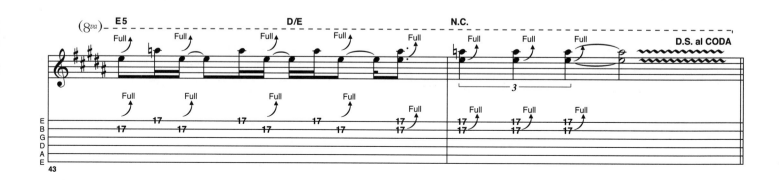

44

My Brother Jake

Words & Music by
Paul Rodgers & Andy Fraser

14G

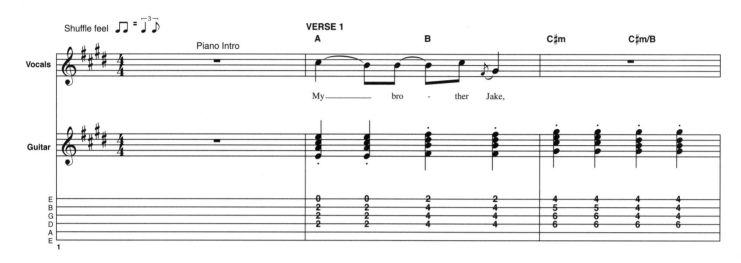

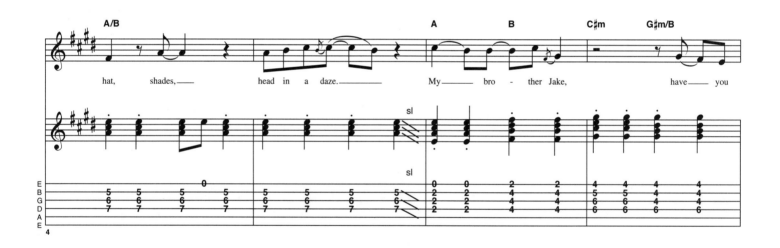

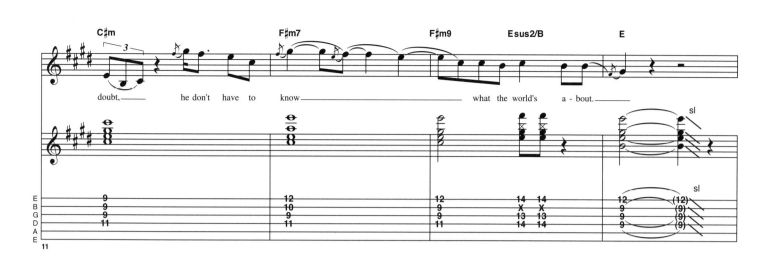

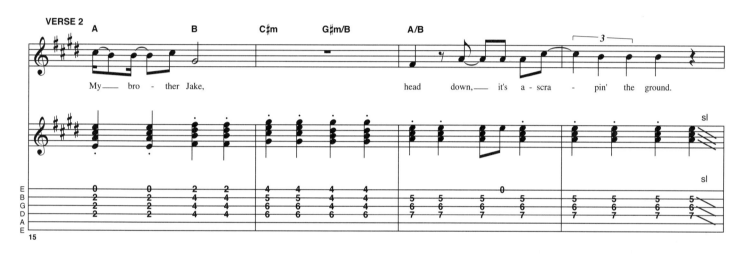

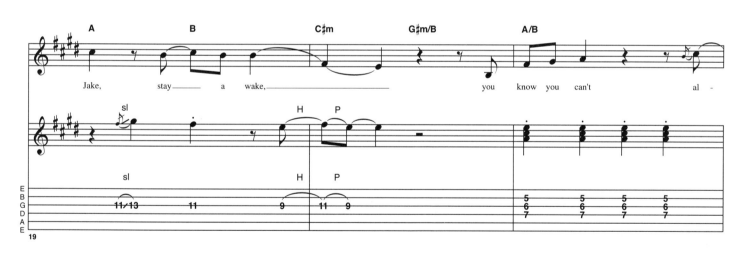

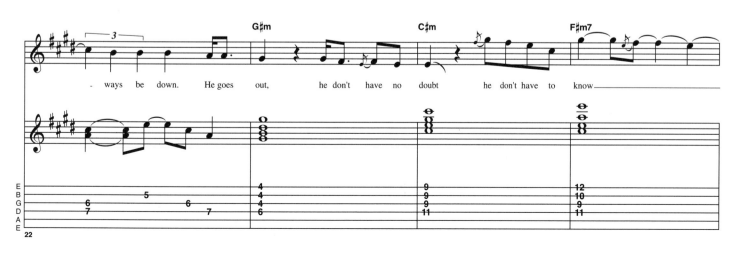

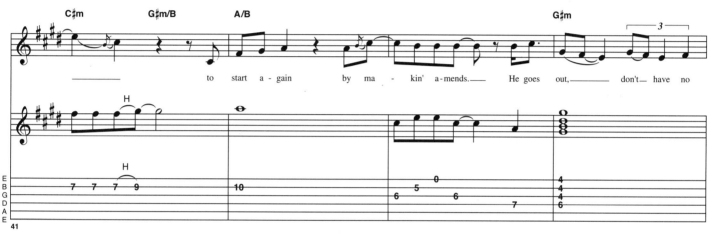

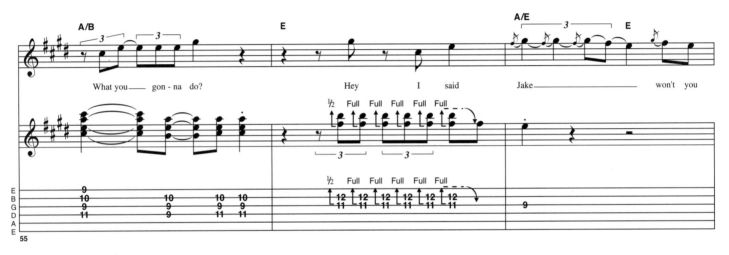

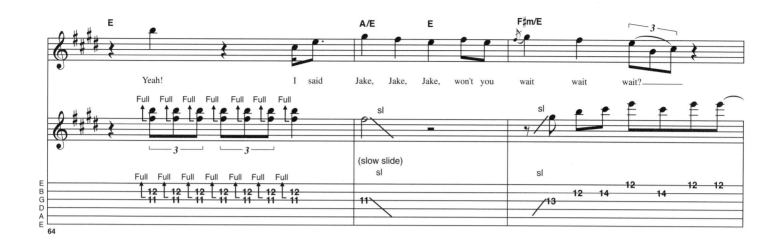

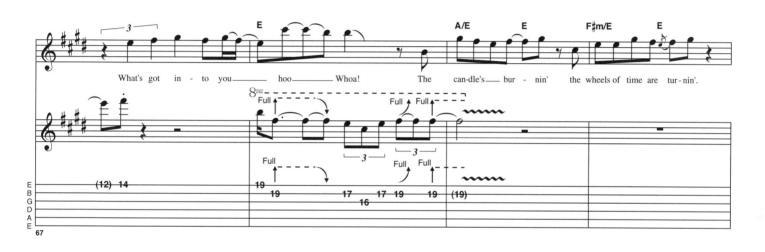

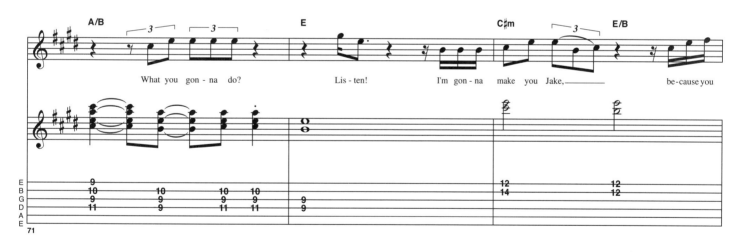

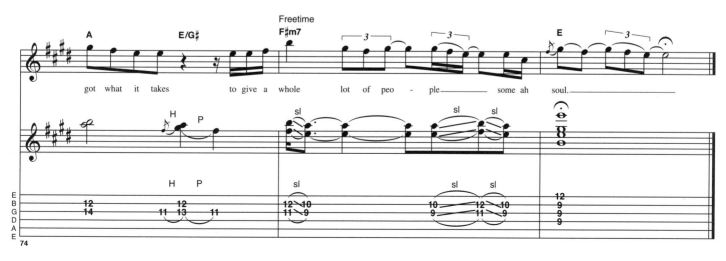

The Stealer

Words & Music by
Paul Rodgers, Andy Fraser & Paul Kossoff

15

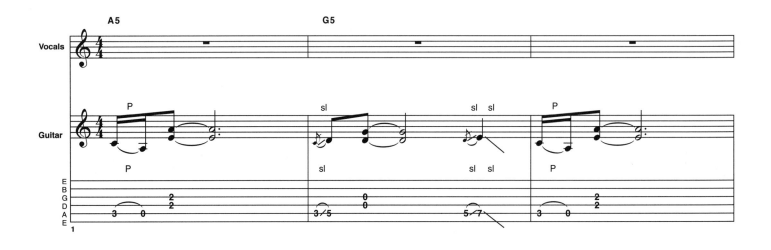

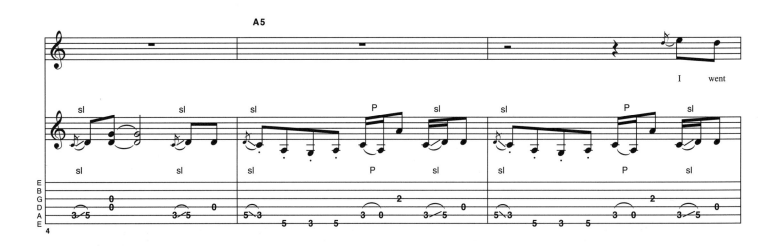

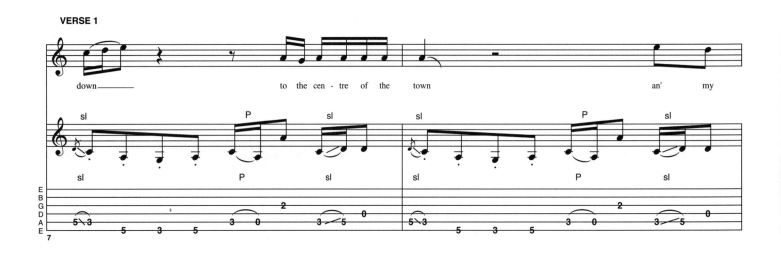

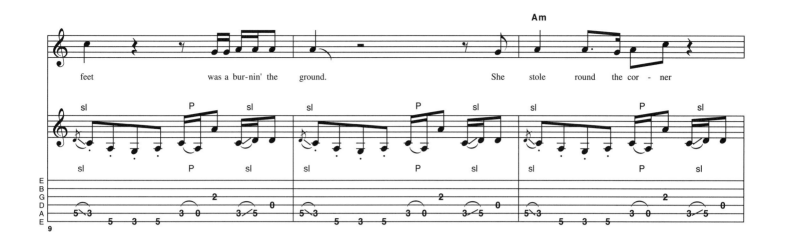

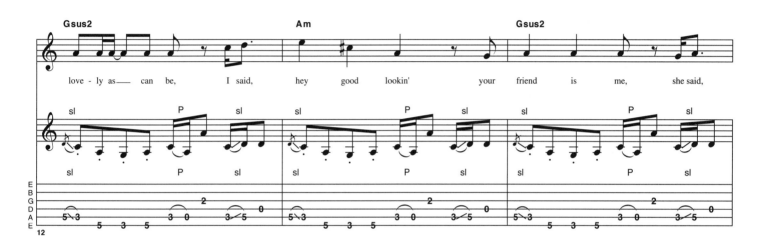

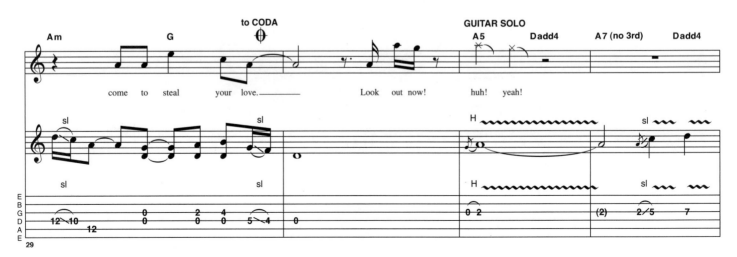

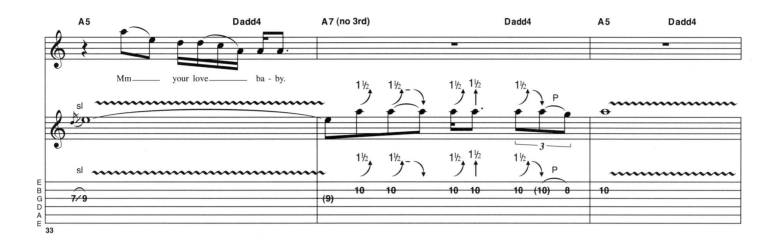

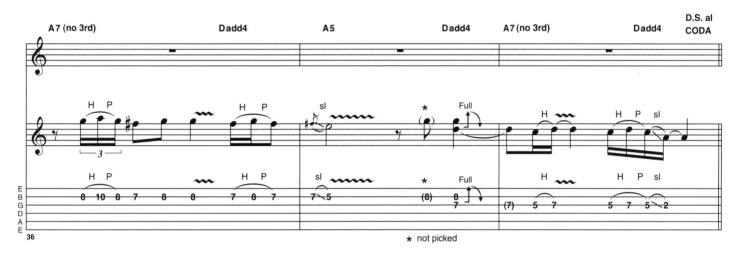

★ not picked

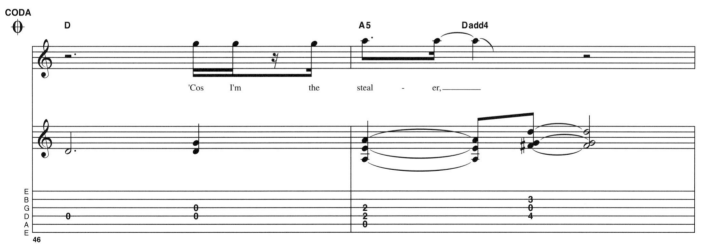

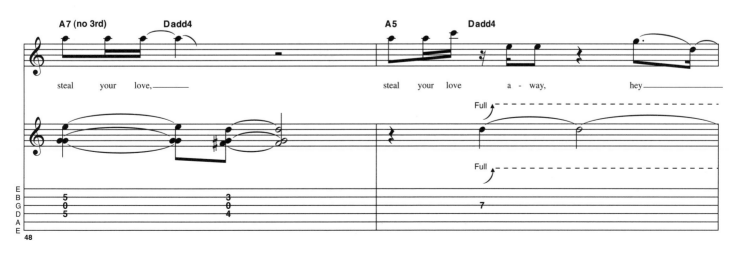

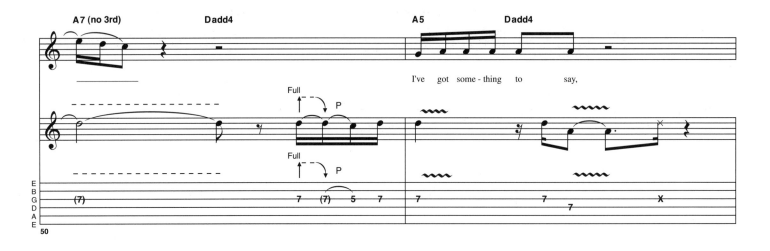

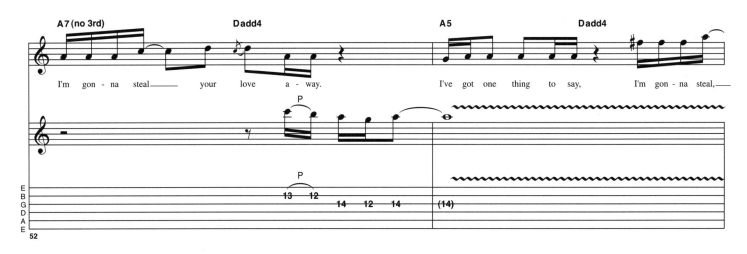

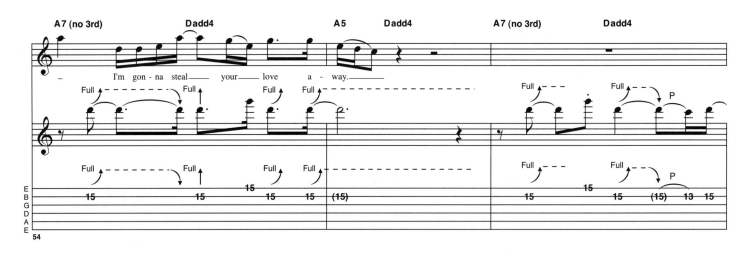

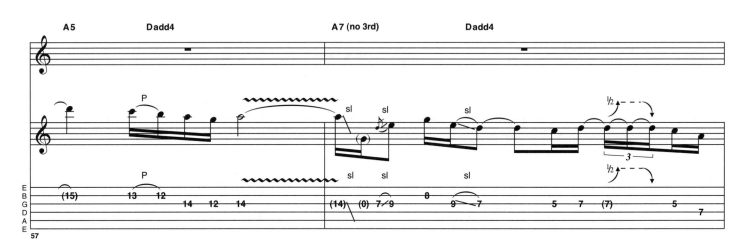

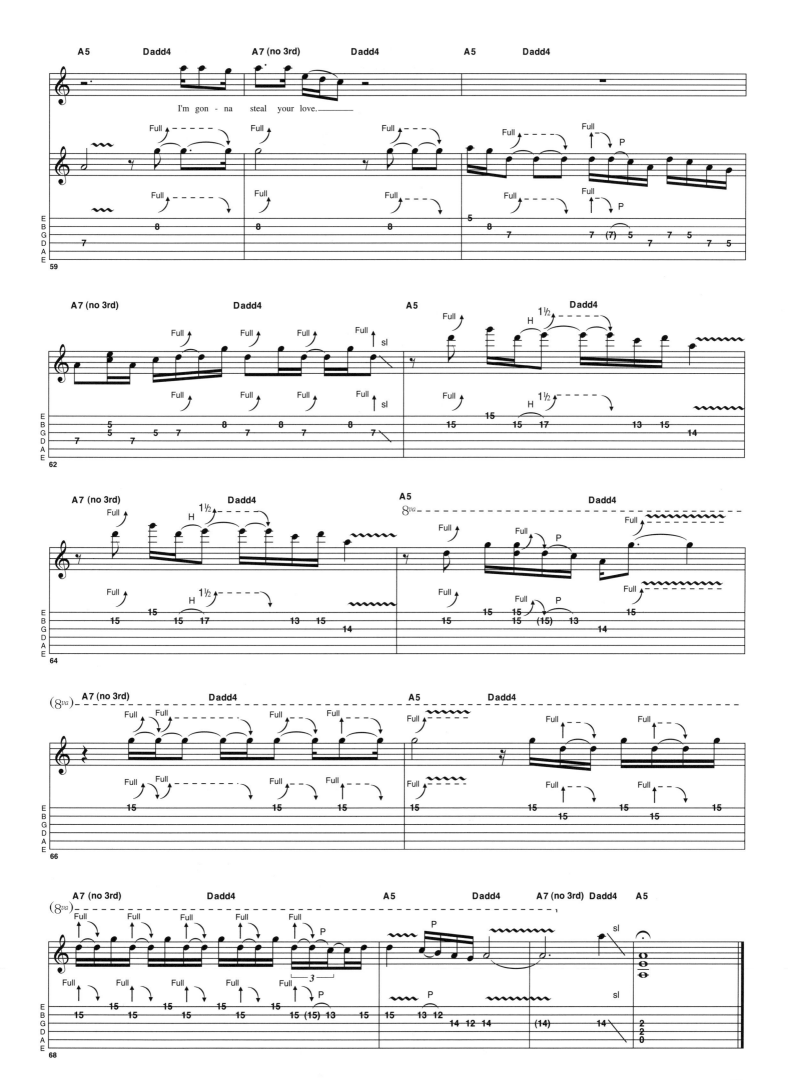

I'm gon - na steal your love.

I'm A Mover

Words & Music by
Paul Rodgers & Andy Fraser

16G

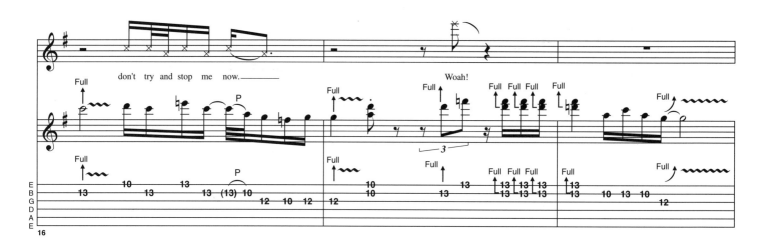

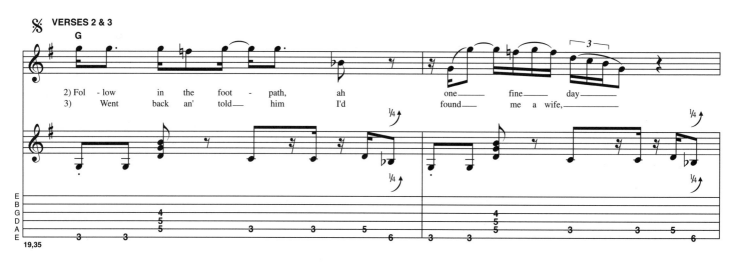

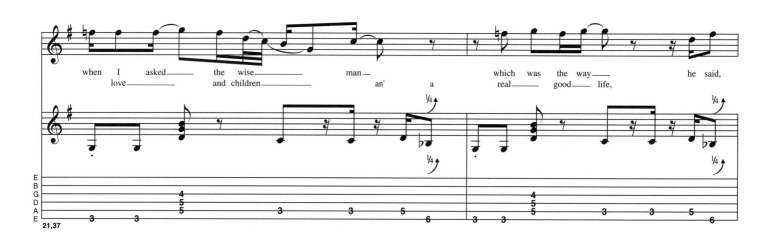

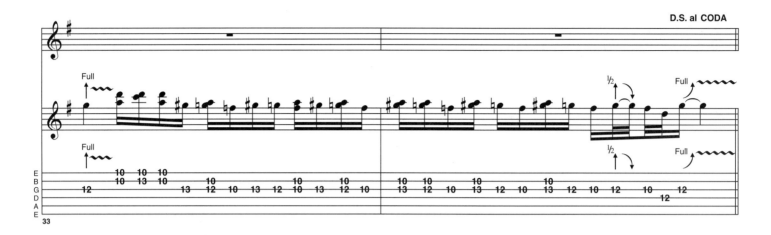

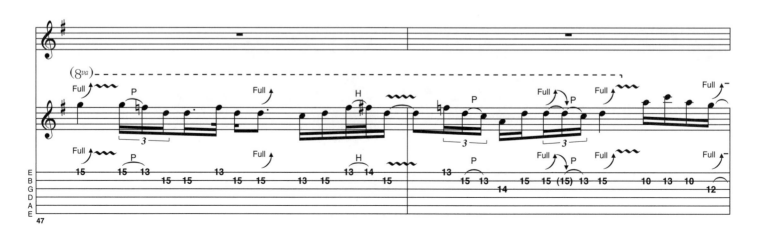

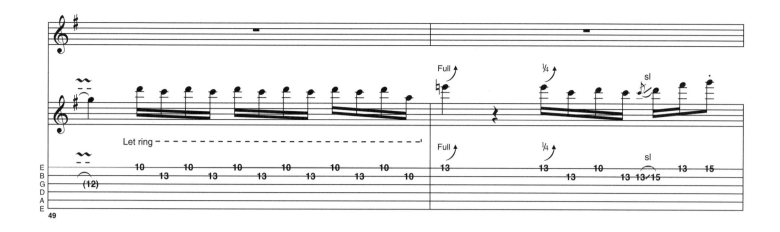

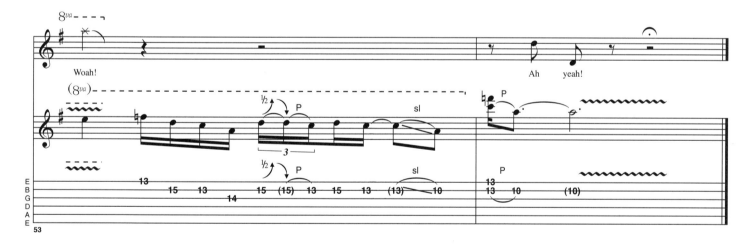